Grade 5-6

CAPTAIN JOHN SMITH'S PAGE

CAPTAIN JOHN SMITH'S PAGE

BY MARION NESBITT

PICTURES BY
DOUGLAS GORSLINE

J. B. LIPPINCOTT COMPANY
PHILADELPHIA AND NEW YORK

177

Stanzas 1 and 2 of "Southern Ships and Settlers"
reprinted from A BOOK OF AMERICANS by
Rosemary and Stephen Vincent Benét, Rinehart
& Company, copyright 1933 by Rosemary and
Stephen Vincent Benét.

The records of the Colony of Virginia tell that Samuel Collier was one of four "boyes" who came with
the first settlers to Jamestown in May, 1607; that he
was Captain John Smith's page; that in December,
1608, he was left with the king of the Waraskoyacks
to "learne the language;" and that in 1622 he was
". . . one of our most ancientist Planters . . . and
Governor of a Towne."

CONTENTS

O, where are you going, "Goodspeed" and
    "Discovery"?
With meek "Susan Constant" to make up the
    three?
We're going to settle the wilds of Virginia,
For gold and adventure we're crossing the
    sea.

And what will you find there? Starvation and
    fever.
We'll eat of the adder and quarrel and rail.
All but sixty shall die of the first seven hun-
    dred,
But a nation begins with the voyage we sail.

I. FAR-OFF VIRGINIA

Samuel Collier walked the streets of London looking for work to help him earn his bread. Samuel was ten years old and tall and strong for his age. He was fair-skinned and fair-haired. His sea-blue English eyes were clear, and quick to see all that was going on around him.

Samuel's father was dead. His stepmother had said that a lad of ten years who could already read and write should go to work. But work was hard to find and Samuel had not a penny in his pockets.

As he walked through the narrow streets of London filled with horses and carts and people, Samuel heard wonderful tales of a tall brave soldier with sharp blue eyes and a big red beard. This soldier was Captain John Smith. He had fought in many wars in many lands. He had fought pirates, he had been shipwrecked, and he had killed three Turks with his sword.

Now John Smith was making ready to start on another adventure. He was going to sail across the Atlantic Ocean to the far-off land of Virginia.

The London Company was sending out three ships, loaded with men and food and tools and guns. They were going to start an English colony in that land of dark forests, Indians, and wild beasts.

For a long time Englishmen had dreamed of planting a colony in the New World but the dream had never come true. The London Company hoped that this time the dream would come true and that they would become rich. In London it was said that gold and pearls could be found lying around on the ground in that far-off country.

James the First, the King of England, said the London Company could plant a colony in Virginia but he would not give them any money to outfit the ships. But he also said, if they found any gold or pearls, they would have to give the crown its share.

As he walked along the street to a blacksmith's shop he knew Samuel thought of all the stories he had heard about Virginia. Maybe the blacksmith would let him blow the hot coals with his bellows and pay him a penny for his work.

He found the shop and walked in. He waited while the blacksmith talked to a gentleman about a sword he held in his hand.

Samuel looked hard at the gentleman. His heart seemed to stand still. The gentleman was tall, he had sharp blue eyes, and a big red beard. Could it be Captain John Smith?

Samuel forgot all about blowing the bellows. When the gentleman walked out of the shop, Samuel was close behind him. When he reached the street Samuel came beside him and said, "Sir, could you be Captain John Smith who is going to Virginia?"

The gentleman turned and looked at Samuel. " 'Tis just what I plan to do, boy, but who are you?"

"I am Samuel Collier and I would like to go with you."

The captain laughed and said, "Well-spoken, my new friend. A lad who loves adventure is one I am sure to like. I do need a page, but what of your father and mother? And can you read and write?"

Then Samuel told Master Smith of his life and how he would like to seek his fortune in the New World. And so it was that Samuel Collier also made ready to go to Virginia.

On a cold day in February, 1607, the three ships, the *Susan Constant,* the *Goodspeed,* and the *Discovery* set sail for Virginia. Samuel and Captain John Smith were on the *Susan Constant,* the largest of the ships. The ships were in charge of Captain Christopher Newport. Newport was a man of good sense, brave, and a fine seaman.

On board were over a hundred men. There

were no women or girls but there were three
other boys besides Samuel. One of the boys was
named Dicky Mutton and he and Samuel soon
became friends. Samuel had another friend on
board. He was Master Robert Hunt, a minister.
Master Hunt did everything he could to help all
the colonists. They called him "good Master
Hunt."

The voyage was long and it was stormy. Captain Smith kept Samuel busy going on errands
and copying the notes he was always making.
Sometimes he wrote about the sea, sometimes
about strange birds, and sometimes about the
things that were happening on board the ship.

For more than two months the little ships cut
through the waves. Everyone was tired of the
long journey and everyone wished for the sight
of land. Some thought they would never see land
again. Some wished they were back in England.
But the little ships went on.

On April 26 at four o'clock in the morning, the
sleeping passengers heard a great glad shout—
"Land Ho-o! Land Ho-o!" The land of Virginia
had been sighted at last.

Everyone ran on deck. Everyone was shouting

and laughing and talking. Samuel crowded close to the deck rail to look. In the dim morning light he saw a long gray coastline and tall trees. As he stared and stared, he wondered what his fortune would be in this strange land so far from his home.

The ships sailed into the bay the Indians called the Chesapeake. The colonists saw a point of land. They named it Cape Henry after King James' son.

There on Cape Henry the ships dropped anchor and a group of men went on land to explore. They explored all day.

They saw great sand dunes and tall trees covered with vines. They saw fields of flowers. Birds with bright feathers flew in and out among the trees. Some were black with red wings, and others were pale blue, yellow, and green.

They saw squirrels and wild turkeys' nests filled with eggs. They saw all these things but they did not see any Indians. But an Indian saw them. He ran swiftly and quietly through the trees. He carried the news that strange men with white faces had landed.

Late that evening, as the Englishmen were

going on board their ships, the Indians came on all-fours, like bears, with their arrows in their mouths. Suddenly the Indians rose to their feet, fitted arrows to bows and let fly. The arrows fell thick and fast. Two of the explorers were wounded. The ship's cannon boomed out and the Indians ran back into the forest.

The next day the colonists sailed up a broad river. They named it the James in honor of their king. For over two weeks they explored, looking for a good place to land and to build their town. At last the ships came close to the shore and were tied to big trees on the bank.

On May 14, the gangplanks were lowered, trumpets blew a loud ta-ta-ta-ta-ta, and everyone stepped ashore.

These men and boys of England who had come so far to the land of Virginia, stood still and looked about them. The sun was shining, the air was soft and sweet, and the trees were a deep green. Flowers grew everywhere. The dogwood and the redbud were in bloom and mocking birds sang in the trees.

Samuel Collier thought he could never stop

looking. He thought it must be like heaven come
to earth. As he looked Master Hunt raised his
hand. The colonists fell on their knees. Samuel
knelt and bowed his head. He heard the minister
saying,

> O Lord, we beseech thee mercifully to hear us;
> and grant that we, by thy mighty aid, be de-
> fended and comforted in all dangers and adver-
> sities . . . Amen.

The colonists rose to their feet and began the
work of building Jamestown.

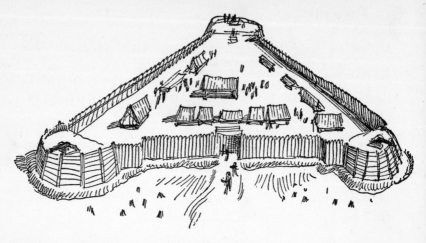

II. POCAHONTAS

Men ran here and there, unloading supplies, cutting down trees, and putting up tents. Samuel helped Master Smith build their hut of branches cut from the trees.

He also helped Master Hunt. The minister was stretching an old sailcloth between trees to make a church. Samuel helped him put logs under the sailcloth for the colonists to sit on.

As the sun went down the tired men and boys gathered together under the old sail to listen to Master Hunt and to say their evening prayers. Soon afterwards they fell asleep on their beds of pine needles and green leaves.

The last sounds Samuel heard that night were

those of the flowing river and the wind in the trees.

For days the work of building Jamestown went on. Everybody was happy and full of hope. Samuel did not see any gold or pearls but he was so busy he did not have time to think of them. He had come to seek his fortune in this new land and he believed he would find it.

As soon as the first houses were finished, work began on the fort to be built around the town. It was in the shape of a triangle and made of pointed logs. It was called a palisade.

In each of the three corners there was a watch-tower with cannon and big guns. Night and day someone must keep watch.

Captain Newport, Captain Smith, and some of the other men explored up and down the James River. They visited Indian towns and tried to make friends with the Indians.

Samuel wished that he could go, too. Then one day, Captain Smith told him that he could go with them to visit the king of the Rappahannas. This king lived on the other side of the James River. They sailed across the river until they came to the Indian town.

The king, playing on a flute made of reeds and with all his people following him, came dancing down to the waterside.

He wore a crown of deer hair, colored red in the fashion of a rose. On one side of his head he wore a large plate of copper. Two long feathers like horns were fastened to the top of his head. His body was painted crimson and his face blue. He had a chain of beads around his neck and his ears were hung with loops of pearls.

The Englishmen followed the king to his town. Here they sat on mats. The king smoked a pipe filled with tobacco, and then passed it to the white men to smoke.

The Indian women brought great baskets of deer meat and bread. The Indian girls brought strawberries and blueberries for the visitors to eat.

Captain Newport and Captain Smith gave the Indians presents of pins and needles, little bells, and colored beads.

Samuel looked at the Indian boys. He wished he could talk to them. He wondered if he would ever learn their language. His master was already learning to talk to the Indians. Because he could talk to them, Smith had learned that the greatest chief in all Virginia was named Powhatan. He was king of thirty tribes and he lived in a place called Werowocomoco.

The feast lasted for hours. When it was over, white men and Indians promised to be friends always. The Indians walked to the riverside and watched the white men get in their boats and sail back to Jamestown.

A few days later Captain Newport sailed back to England. He took with him the *Susan Constant* and the *Goodspeed*. He left the *Discovery*, the smallest of the ships, for the colonists to use.

All the colonists stood on the shore to wave goodbye as the two ships dropped down the James to the open sea.

Samuel felt sad and alone. He looked at his master. The captain was not smiling, but as always his blue eyes looked brave and strong. Smith turned his eyes from the river and looked at Samuel. Then side by side master and page walked back to the fort.

Soon after Newport had gone, the colonists found that they had little food left. The Indians would not trade with them. The only food they could get was fish from the river.

Every time the Englishmen went outside the palisade they were in great danger. The Indians who lived near Jamestown hid in the tall grass and behind the trees and shot at them.

The summer sun was very hot and mosquitoes were everywhere. They stung the colonists and caused them to have fever and chills. Before the summer was over there were only six men strong enough to work or watch beside the big guns.

When September came almost half of the colonists had died. Some had starved to death and the others had died from sickness and wounds.

Dicky Mutton, Samuel's friend, had died. Another boy, James Brumfield, had been killed by an Indian arrow. But Samuel Collier lived through it all.

As the cool fall days came and the mosquitoes were gone, things began to get better. The river and the sky were full of ducks and geese on their way to the south for the winter. Now the starving colonists had something to eat besides fish.

Then a strange thing happened.

The Indians came in great crowds to Jamestown. They came bringing deer meat and beans and bread, ready cooked.

The sick began to get well. And once again everybody became happy and hopeful. They set to work to make better houses and a better church. They made the fort stronger and cleaned up the streets of Jamestown.

As winter came on food began to give out again. Captain John Smith decided to do something about it. He took some men with him and they sailed up and down the rivers looking for Indian towns.

They traded hatchets and knives and copper and beads for great baskets of corn. The corn would be made into bread for the hungry colonists.

On a trip in the cold of December, Captain Smith was captured by the Indians. He had left his men on the boat while he went exploring with an Indian guide. The king of the Pamunkey Indians with two hundred of his men came out of the woods with their bows and arrows and surrounded Smith and took him prisoner.

The men in the boat sailed back to Jamestown to tell what had happened. They were sure the Indians had killed Smith.

Everyone ran to meet the men as they came into the palisade. Their faces were sad as they heard the story. Nicolas Skot, the drummer, beat a sad roll on the drum he had brought with him from England. The colonists turned away to go back to their work.

Samuel felt as if his heart would break. Master Hunt held out his hand to him and said, "And now, Sammy, you must live with me."

So Samuel went to live with good Master Hunt.

One week passed, two weeks, three weeks. Then, one day, there was a loud cry from the sentry in the watchtower. Everyone ran to the big gate to look. There was John Smith alive and well! With him were four Indians. One carried his knapsack, two carried great baskets of bread and one walked by Smith's side.

Samuel ran to meet his master. Smith put his hand on the boy's shoulder. He laughed and said, "Not this time, Sammy. I hope I will be with you for a long time to come."

Smith had a wonderful story to tell. The Indians had taken him from town to town to show him off. The women and children would run out to stare at him.

At last they took him to their great king, Powhatan, who lived at Werowocomoco.

Smith was taken into Powhatan's long house. The great king sat on a big bed, covered with skins. The room was crowded with Indian bowmen, women, and children.

Smith knew that the Indians loved to make long speeches. Sometimes they would talk for hours before they would trade.

So Smith told Powhatan of the roundness of the earth. He told him of the moon and the stars and the planets. He showed him his compass. Powhatan tried to touch the needle and for the first time in his life touched glass.

Powhatan told Smith of his great lands and of great rivers dashing over stones. He told of other rivers flowing from great mountains between two seas.

Smith then told of England and his great king. He told of his king's big ships, the noise of many trumpets and the Englishmen's way of fighting with swords, pistols and cannon.

At last Powhatan made a sign to his guards. They took hold of Smith and pushed his head down on a big stone. Other guards raised their heavy clubs to kill him.

Just then a girl ran out from beside Powhatan and threw her arms around Smith. The Indians dropped their clubs. The girl was Pocahontas, Powhatan's favorite child. She was about twelve years old.

She liked this stranger with the white skin and the red beard. She did not want him to die. So Smith's life was saved and Powhatan had let him come back to Jamestown.

That winter Pocahontas came often to the fort. She came with her maidens, carrying great baskets of corn and other food for the hungry colonists.

She would stand outside the gate of the fort and call for Captain Smith. She would not come in until he came.

Samuel saw Pocahontas each time she came to Jamestown. She would smile at him but say nothing. One day she gave him two eagle feathers and he gave her a little glass bell that made a tiny tinkling sound.

When the warm days of spring and summer came, the colonists planted gardens. They planted corn and beans. Some of them planted little patches of the Indian weed, tobacco.

Samuel was growing tall and strong and his skin was tanned by the wind and the sun. He learned to paddle a canoe and to fish in the river. He learned to bake bread on hot stones and roast oysters as the Indians did.

In the autumn of 1608, in September, Captain John Smith was made president of the colony.

The news made Samuel very happy. He thought his master was the bravest and finest man in all Jamestown. Smith knew better than anyone else how to trade with the Indians and how to keep them from attacking Jamestown.

The Indians tried many times to kill Smith, but each time he was able to save himself. He was so brave and so quick in danger that the Indians feared him. They thought he was a kind of god.

Smith was hard working and he knew how to get things done. He had a new storehouse built for the corn he planned to get from the Indians. Winter was coming and the colonists did not have enough food to last until spring.

Smith made the men drill every day so they would be ready to fight if the Indians attacked. He told those who would not work that they should not eat.

Besides keeping things going at Jamestown, Smith went on many trading trips. He also explored the rivers of Virginia and the Chesapeake Bay. He made maps and wrote about what he had seen so the people in England would know more about the land of Virginia.

Smith and the other colonists wanted England

to claim a part of this New World. The Spanish king had claimed a large part of it and the Spanish colonies were growing. The people at Jamestown always feared that Spanish ships would come sailing up the James and take their land away from them and make all of them prisoners.

When October came and the trees were red and gold in the woods, Captain Newport came sailing back to Virginia. He brought a shipload of settlers and supplies.

On board were two women, Mistress Forrest

and her maid. They were the first women to come to Virginia.

There were also some Germans, whom the colonists called Dutchmen, and some Poles on the ship. They were brought over to make glass, and pitch, and tar.

The colonists built a house they called the Glasshouse about a mile from Jamestown. The London Company wanted them to make glass and send it back to England to be sold.

Samuel often walked along the little path through the woods to the Glasshouse. He liked to see the men at their work. Sometimes he helped them take the glass from the big oven and put it in the cooling oven. To do this he had to use a long stick, curved at the end.

There was something about the Glasshouse that Samuel did not understand. Often the Dutchmen and the Poles whispered together.

One day Samuel saw one of the Dutchmen go into the woods and give something to an Indian who had been hiding behind a tree. When the Dutchman came back he said he had gone to the woods to gather walnuts.

Samuel did not believe what the man said. He knew the Poles and Dutchmen did not like Jamestown and they wanted to leave as soon as they could. Samuel wanted to tell his master about this but Smith was away on a trading trip. When he got back, there was no time to tell him about the Dutchmen, for he had to go at once to Powhatan's town.

III. THE CROWNING OF POWHATAN

Captain Newport had brought something from England besides settlers and supplies. He had brought gifts for Powhatan. He brought a bedstead and a basin and pitcher. He brought a scarlet robe embroidered with gold thread, and a gilded crown, set with glass jewels.

The people in England did not understand the Indians. They did not know what they were like. The king of England and the London Company

thought that the gifts and the crown would keep
Powhatan from attacking the English settlers.

Captain John Smith knew that this was foolish.
He was sure that the old chief would know at
once why the king was sending him gifts. Smith
did not want to crown Powhatan but he knew
he and Newport must do what the king wished.

Newport asked Smith to go overland to Werowocomoco and invite Powhatan to come to Jamestown for the coronation. So Smith set out with
three men and his page to invite Powhatan to
come to Jamestown.

Samuel was delighted to be going. He had
never seen the great Powhatan and he had never
been to Werowocomoco.

Powhatan's town was about twelve miles from
Jamestown. It was on the far side of a large
river. The English named the river the York.

Smith, the three men, and Samuel walked for
miles along the Indian trails through the thick
woods.

Squirrels, rabbits, and deer ran across their
path. Red and gold and brown leaves fell from
the trees. The woods smelled of pine needles,

rotting sticks, toadstools, and Indian fires.

When they came to the York River they paddled across it in canoes. As they reached the far side, Samuel saw the smoke of many fires and he knew they had at last reached the town of the mighty Powhatan.

The Englishmen saw fields of corn and tobacco. They saw a grove of tall trees. Paths ran in all directions among the trees.

The Englishmen walked along one of the paths, and Samuel saw more Indian houses than he had ever seen before. They were made of curved saplings that had been stuck into the ground and then covered with bark and grass mats. Smoke curled up through holes in the roof.

Indian children were playing under the trees and Indian women with their long black hair hanging around their faces, stood in doorways. The women and children looked scared when they saw the white men.

Smith led his men along another path until they came to a great oak tree. There Samuel saw the largest and longest Indian house he had ever seen. It was the house in which Powhatan lived.

Four sentries were walking back and forth, guarding each corner of the house.

Smith spoke to one of the sentries and told him why they had come. The sentry told Smith that Powhatan was away on a hunting trip but he would send a runner to give him the message.

Another runner was sent to tell all the people in the town that the white men had come.

The men from Jamestown were led to an open field with a fire in the middle of it. They sat down on mats around the fire. The women and the children and the men who had not gone hunting sat down also.

Suddenly from the woods there came a great noise of yelling and shrieking.

The Englishmen thought they were being attacked by Powhatan. But it was not Indian men who made the noise. It was Pocahontas, leading thirty of her maidens in a wild dance.

The girls wore green leaves around their waists. Their bodies were painted white and red and black. They carried wooden swords, clubs and sticks.

Pocahontas had a pair of deer horns on her head. She had an otter skin around her waist and another on her arm. A quiver full of arrows was on her back and in her hands she carried a bow.

The girls whirled and danced and yelled around the fire for nearly an hour. Then suddenly they ran into the woods.

In a little while they came back, walking slowly and quietly. This time they wore everyday Indian clothes. Then they helped the Indian women make a feast for the white men.

The girls brought great baskets of bread and wooden platters of fish and deer meat. They brought beans and peas and nuts.

The feast lasted until the night came and the stars came out. The Indian boys and girls took lighted sticks from the fire and showed the white men where they could sleep.

That night, for the first time in his life, Samuel Collier slept in an Indian house.

The next day came Powhatan. Samuel was almost afraid to look at him. The great chief was tall and straight and about seventy years old. His face was stern and his black eyes were as keen as a hawk's. He wore a raccoon coat with the tails hanging around the bottom. In his hair were three eagle feathers.

Powhatan, with his guard of fifty bowmen, the tallest men in his kingdom, walked toward Smith.

Smith told Powhatan that his royal brother, the King of England, had sent him gifts and a gilded crown to wear on his head. He told him that Captain Newport wanted him to come to Jamestown to be crowned.

Powhatan listened as Smith talked, then he wrapped his raccoon coat about him and said, "If your king has sent me presents, I also am a king, and this is my land. Your Captain Newport must come to me, not I to him. Nor will I go to your fort, neither will I bite at such a bait."

So Captain John Smith, the three men, and Samuel had to go back to Jamestown without Powhatan.

When Newport heard what had happened, he decided to send the gifts by water to Werowoco-moco. He and Smith and Samuel with fifty men, the best shots at Jamestown, went overland to Powhatan's town.

When they reached Werowocomoco all of Powhatan's people, men, women, and children were crowded together to watch the coronation.

The boat with the gifts on board was anchored by the town. The sailors were ready to fire a salute from the big guns as soon as the crown was put on Powhatan's head. The fifty men from Jamestown were lined up, some to blow trumpets and some to fire guns.

Smith and Newport stood by Powhatan's side. Samuel sat by Pocahontas and her young brother.

Newport had workmen from the ship set up the bedstead for Powhatan. The old chief looked at

the bedstead but he did not touch it. He did not touch the basin and pitcher when they were set down near him.

Then Newport put the scarlet robe around Powhatan's shoulders. Powhatan seemed to like the robe. Newport then took the gilded crown from a velvet box and told Powhatan to kneel and bow his head. The Indian king would not move.

Smith tried to show him what to do. Powhatan would not move.

Samuel looked at Pocahontas. She was laughing and Samuel laughed, too.

At last Smith and two other men pushed hard on Powhatan's shoulders. Newport quickly put the crown on his head, but it was crooked and almost fell off.

The trumpets blew a loud blast, the men fired their guns, and the ship's cannon boomed a salute. Powhatan, the King of Virginia, had become the royal brother of the King of England.

When all the guns and trumpets had become quiet, Powhatan looked around to see what he could give the Englishmen. He spied his old raccoon coat and a pair of his old shoes. These he gave to Newport with a few ears of corn. And that was all the Englishmen got by crowning Powhatan.

Not long after the crowning of Powhatan Captain Newport went back to England. He left seventy new settlers for the colony. Now there were two hundred people living at Jamestown.

Winter was near. The wind blew cold and the storehouse was almost empty. Many baskets of corn would be needed to feed two hundred hungry people.

Smith and some of his men sailed in the *Discovery* to nearby Indian towns, trying to trade for corn. But the Indians seemed more ready to fight than trade.

Powhatan had ordered his tribes not to trade with the Englishmen. He wanted them to starve. So the boats came back to Jamestown empty.

Samuel did all he could to help his master. He cut wood and stacked it in big piles for the winter. He helped some of the men shell what corn was left in the storehouse. When his master was away he ran errands for Master Hunt and the sentries on the palisade.

One day, when Samuel was talking to a sentry, he saw an Indian come toward the big gate in the fort.

The sentry called the Indian to halt. The Indian said he wanted to talk to Captain Smith. Samuel ran to get his master.

The Indian told Smith that he brought a message from Powhatan. Powhatan wanted an English house with a chimney and a fireplace, and a door with a lock and key. He also wanted a grindstone, fifty swords, some guns, and a cock and a hen. If Smith would send men to build the house in the woods near Werowocomoco, and bring the other gifts, Powhatan would load his boats with corn.

Smith told the Indian he would send men by land at once to build the house. Then he and other men would come by boat for the corn. He said he would bring the grindstone and the cock and hen but he had no guns or swords to spare.

The Indian started back to Powhatan's town with the message and Smith went at once to choose workmen to build the house. He decided to send four of the Dutchmen and one Englishman.

The workmen set out the next day. Smith then ordered men to get the *Discovery* and two other smaller boats ready for the trip.

On the twenty-ninth of December, Smith with forty-six men and Samuel Collier set sail for Werowocomoco.

It was early in the morning when the ships started down the James. The sky was gray and a strong wind was blowing. It began to rain, the rain changed to sleet, and then it began to snow.

Smith decided they would tie up for the night at an Indian town called Waraskoyack. The king of this town was Tackonekintaco. He had always been a friend of the English.

Smith thought that here he would be able to trade with Tackonekintaco for enough food to last until they came to Werowocomoco.

The Englishmen stepped ashore in the snow. The wind was icy. Samuel pulled his coat close around him and bowed his head as he walked.

Smith and his men went at once to the king's long house. Tackonekintaco was glad to see Smith. He told the Englishmen they could spend the night in his town. He also said that he would let them have enough food for their journey.

Samuel was glad to come in out of the cold. A bright fire burned in the middle of the house. The room was dry and warm and smoky. No rain, or wind, or snow could come through the thick bark and grass mats that covered it.

The Englishmen were hungry. They had not had much to eat this winter and now it was the week of Christmas.

Samuel thought of Christmas in England. He thought of roast goose and plum pudding and boys and girls singing "God Rest Ye Merry, Gentlemen." He wondered if the Indian children would like the story of the star and the baby in the manger. As he looked at the bark walls of the Indian house, England and Christmas seemed far, far away.

While the Englishmen were warming themselves at the fire, a boy came into the long house. He was about the size of Samuel. He was the son of the Indian king and his name was Weanock.

The Indian boy looked at Samuel and smiled, then he came and sat down on a mat close to the one Samuel sat on.

In a little while Indian women came into the long house with big baskets and platters of food. They brought oysters, fish, and deer meat. They brought roast turkey and good fresh bread.

Everybody ate and ate. The men from Jamestown said they had never had better food, or better fires at Christmas time in all of England.

When they had eaten and were sitting around the fire talking, the Indian king said to Smith, "Captain Smith, do not go to Werowocomoco. Do not trust Powhatan. Do not let him have a chance to take your swords and guns. He has sent for you to cut your throats."

Smith thanked Tackonekintaco for telling him this. He said that he would ever be on his guard but that he must get corn or the colony would starve.

That night the Englishmen slept in Indian houses warmed by Indian fires. Samuel slept on a pile of deer skins close by Weanock's side.

IV. ALONE WITH THE INDIANS

The next morning the Englishmen made ready to go on with their trip to Werowocomoco.

Samuel saw his master talking to King Tackone-kintaco. As they talked they looked at Samuel. Then Smith and the Indian king walked to where Samuel and Weanock were standing.

The captain put his hand on Samuel's shoulder and said, "Sammy, I want you to stay here and live with Tackonekintaco and his people. I want you to learn the Indian language. When you have learned the language well, I will send for you to come back to Jamestown."

At first Samuel could not believe what he had heard. Leave Captain Smith and leave Jamestown? And live with the Indians? What would it be like? Would the Indians be good to him or would they kill him?

He looked at his master. Smith's eyes were sad. Samuel looked away and did not speak.

His master was talking again, "We need people, Sammy, to speak the Indian language. If we understand them we can be better friends to them, and they to us."

Samuel looked down at the snow-covered ground. He hoped he would not cry. Suppose no one ever came for him. Suppose he had to live with the Indians the rest of his life. He looked up at his master. Clear blue English eyes met clear blue English eyes in a long, long look.

Samuel straightened his shoulders and said, "Sir, if you wish it, I will stay, and do as best I can."

"You are a brave lad, Sammy, all Jamestown

will be proud of you. Be as a son to Tackonekin-taco, and as a brother to Weanock."

Smith put out his hand. Samuel took it and held it hard. There were tears in the boy's eyes but they did not fall.

Then Smith took from his pocket a tin whistle, some brass bells, and a little box of round white beads. "Here, Samuel," he said, "are gifts that you may reward your friends."

Samuel watched his master as he walked away to go on board the *Discovery*. He kept watching as the ship sailed down the James toward the Bay. He watched until he could see no more. When he looked around, Weanock was standing by his side. Together they walked along the path that led to Weanock's house.

When the boys reached the house, they went inside. Weanock gave Samuel clothes just like his own. He gave him a strip of fringed deerskin to wear around his waist. He gave him a heavy deerskin cloak and a pair of shoes lined with fur to wear when he went out-of-doors.

Samuel took off his English clothes and put them away until the day he should return to

Jamestown. He gave Weanock the tin whistle and two brass bells.

At first the winter days and nights were very long for Samuel. He wondered how many months would pass before someone would come for him. And he wondered if his master had forgotten him. If he had to live with the Indians all his life, how would he find his fortune? Samuel did not know.

Weanock stayed with his white brother always and each day he taught him Indian words and Indian ways.

Samuel soon learned to say *attawp* instead of *bow* and *attonce* instead of *arrows*. For *fire* he said *pokatawer*, and for *house* he said *yehawken*.

Every morning and every evening all the Indians bathed in the river. The women and the young children went first, then the men and the older boys.

They splashed around, threw water at each other and laughed and played. When they came out of the water, they lifted up their arms and prayed to the sun.

Samuel went with Weanock. He, too, jumped into the water. When he came out he lifted up

his arms and said a prayer that Master Hunt had taught him.

Weanock's father often took the boys on hunting trips. Samuel learned the tracks of the deer, the rabbit, and the raccoon. He learned to walk through the woods so quietly that not a leaf moved or a twig snapped. He learned to make a fire as the Indians did. He learned to shoot with a bow and arrow.

When they came in from their hunting trips, Weanock's mother would have a hot stew of meat and hominy, baked sweet potatoes, and brown corn pones waiting for them. They would sit around the fire and eat, and talk of what they had done that day.

When the warm spring days came, Weanock taught Samuel how to set the fish traps in the river and how to snare wild turkeys.

In the spring evenings Samuel and Weanock and some of the other Indian boys and girls would sit around the fire out of doors and talk.

Just before they went into their houses for the night the children would say to Samuel, "Now tell us of London Town."

And Samuel would tell them of London Bridge, and the tall church steeples, and the church bells ringing, ringing, ringing. Then he would tell them "Jack and the Beanstalk" and "Dick Whittington and his Cat."

Sometimes Indians from other towns would come to Waraskoyack and Samuel would hear news of what was happening at Jamestown.

One day in the late spring, Pocahontas came to visit at Waraskoyack. She came with her father's trusty messenger, Rawhunt. Rawhunt brought a message from Powhatan to Tackone-kintaco.

Pocahontas was carrying two little baskets filled with strawberries she had picked along the way. She and Samuel and Weanock sat under a tree and ate the strawberries.

Samuel was glad to see Pocahontas for she knew she would always be a friend to his master.

Pocahontas brought Samuel a gift. It was a quiver filled with arrows and it had been made by her father's own arrow maker.

Samuel was very pleased to get such a fine gift. He thanked Pocahontas and then he said, "Wait here, I have something for you."

When he came back again he held in his hand the little box Captain Smith had given him. Samuel held out the box to Pocahontas and said, "Kehaten Pocahontas patiaquah niugh tanks manotyens neer mowchick rawrenock audowgh."

Pocahontas laughed, she was so pleased to hear Samuel speak in her own language. She came to him and took the box. She knew that he had said, "Bid Pocahontas bring hither two little baskets, and I will give her white beads to make her a chain."

When Pocahontas had looked at the beads and thanked Samuel, she said to him, "I have something to tell you. The four Dutchmen who came to build my father the English house are still with him. I do not like them. I do not trust them. They have many guns and swords. I do not know where they get them. Each day they drill my father's men and show them how to fire the guns. I fear they mean to kill Captain Smith."

Samuel was worried when he heard this. He wished there was something he could do about it.

V. TROUBLE IN JAMESTOWN

While Samuel was living with the Indians many things were happening at Jamestown.

When Smith came back from his visit to Powhatan, he found that powder, shot, guns, swords, and tools were disappearing from Jamestown. He could not find out who was stealing them. At last two men who were in the plot became frightened and told Smith what was happening.

The Dutchmen who were with Powhatan, had friends at the Glasshouse helping them. One of the Dutchmen named Francis would disguise himself as an Indian. He would come to the woods near the Glasshouse and his friends would give him the guns and swords. Some of Powhatan's Indians would help him take the stolen goods away.

The Dutchmen had made a plot with Powhatan to kill all the English colonists and burn Jamestown. They had told Powhatan that Spanish ships would come to Virginia and that the Spanish would reward Powhatan for killing the English.

When Smith heard about the plot he sent a man named Volday to Powhatan to get the Dutchmen and bring them back to Jamestown.

Smith did not know it, but Volday was the very man who had been giving the swords and the guns to the Dutchmen. So Volday did not come back but stayed with the Dutchmen.

When Smith and the other colonists found out what Volday had done they were angry.

Smith chose two young men to go to Powhatan to ask him to send the traitors back to Jamestown to be punished. Richard Wiffin and

Jeffrey Abbot, the men he chose, were two of his best friends whom he knew he could trust.

Before Wiffin and Abbot started off, Smith called them to him and said, "Go first to Waraskoyack and get my page, Samuel Collier, to go with you. I think by now he can speak the language well. He will be able to talk with Powhatan. Much depends on what is said to Powhatan and how it is spoken. Samuel is a bright lad and a brave lad, I believe he can act well as my messenger."

Wiffin and Abbot set off for Waraskoyack. When they reached the Indian town, they found Weanock and Samuel fishing in the river.

When Samuel saw the young men he thought he must be dreaming. It had been many months since he had seen a white man.

Wiffin and Abbot told Samuel why they had come.

When Samuel heard what it was Master Smith wanted him to do he was frightened and glad at the same time. Suppose he did not say the right thing. Suppose Powhatan would not listen to a boy. Suppose he would not let any of them come back to Jamestown.

As Samuel thought about these things, he knew that whatever happened he must do it. He knew that however hard it might be he wanted to do it.

He turned to Wiffin and Abbot and said, "When do we start on this journey?"

Wiffin replied, "Master Smith wishes you to start at once. When you have talked with Powhatan, your master wishes you to return to Jamestown with us."

Samuel's heart beat fast. He was going back to Jamestown and work for Master Smith again!

Samuel looked at Weanock. The Indian boy's face was sad. Weanock could not understand all that was said but somehow he knew that Samuel was leaving.

Samuel and Weanock walked back to the house of bark and grass where they had lived together. Samuel went inside. He took off his Indian clothes and put on his English clothes. The English clothes felt tight and strange.

Weanock had gone to get his father. When

Samuel came out of the house he went to tell Tackonekintaco goodbye.

Tackonekintaco looked down at Samuel and said, "Tell Captain Smith I have been as a father to you and you have been to me as a son."

Samuel started down the path that led through the woods with Wiffin and Abbot.

Weanock walked with them until they came to an open field. Here he stopped. Samuel took Weanock's hand. Indian boy and English boy looked hard at each other. For a time neither boy spoke, then Samuel said, "Mawchick chammay."

When Samuel had spoken, Weanock said, "Mawchick chammay."

Each boy knew the other had said, "The best of friends."

It was a journey of two days to Powhatan's town. All along the way, Samuel was thinking of what he would say to Powhatan. He hoped he would say the right thing. He did not like to think about what would happen if he should make a mistake.

When Samuel and the two men reached the

town they went at once to Powhatan's house. The four sentries walked back and forth as always.

Samuel told a sentry they would like to see Powhatan. The sentry went into the house. After a while he returned and told the Englishmen that the king would see them.

Powhatan sat on his big bed. The bed was covered with skins and pillows of leather, embroidered with pearls. Around Powhatan were many women and children. Samuel saw Pocahontas not far from her father. Up and down the sides of the long house stood Powhatan's bowmen.

In the corners of the room were long poles with scalps hanging from them. Along the walls on both sides were lighted torches. The room smelled of leather, tobacco, and wood fires.

Samuel came near to Powhatan. Powhatan raised his hand and said, "Why have you come?"

"I have come from Captain Smith to bring you a message."

Powhatan said, "What is the message you bring?"

Samuel took a deep breath, he stood tall and straight and said, "Powhatan, you know that Captain Smith has long been your friend."

Powhatan replied, "You know that I did always make him welcome and ever had him sit beside me."

Then Samuel thought of the way his master and Powhatan would always talk, back and forth, back and forth, before they ever began to trade. So Samuel began to talk as much like Captain

Smith as he could and Powhatan began to answer.

Samuel: You know that Captain Smith did give you a suit of red cloth, a white greyhound, and a hat.

Powhatan: I did give him bread, deer meat, and a turkey cock.

Samuel: He did give you a great gun and a grindstone.

Powhatan: When Captain Smith came to trade I had my people bring great baskets of corn. His visits did much content me.

Samuel: He had the Dutchmen build you an English house with chimney and with fireplace. He did not call you stranger but always called you friend.

Powhatan: I did call him son and saved him from death because my daughter asked it.

Samuel: These same Dutchmen who built your house now plot to kill him and all the rest of us and to fire our town. You did promise him friendship and the friendship of your people. It is fit for kings to keep their promises.

Powhatan sat taller and straighter than ever. His stern face looked sterner than ever. He turned to two of his guards and said, "Bring in the Dutchmen and Volday."

In a short while the guards returned with the Dutchmen and Volday. The guards pushed them in front of Powhatan.

The traitors gave one look at Powhatan's cold, hard face and they all began to talk at once. The Dutchmen said it was all Volday's doing. Volday said it was the Dutchmen who planned it. Each one blamed the other and each one tried to save himself.

Powhatan listened for a while, then a look of disgust came over his face. He raised his hand and the Dutchmen stopped talking.

Powhatan's black hawk eyes seemed to look through them. Then the Indian king said, "Traitors, all of you. You who would have betrayed Captain Smith to me, will certainly betray me. You well deserve the punishment you shall receive."

Powhatan then turned to Samuel and said, "Tell Captain Smith I do not wish to keep these traitors, nor will I keep anyone to give him displeasure."

Samuel's face lighted up and he said, "Powhatan, Captain Smith will ever be grateful to you for what you have done this day."

Powhatan almost smiled at the boy. He said, "Tell Captain Smith you have been a good messenger."

Not long after Wiffin and Abbot and Samuel had started on their way back to Jamestown, Powhatan ordered his guards to bring in a large stone, raise their heavy clubs and beat the traitors to death.

When Samuel and the two men came in sight of Jamestown, the guard on the watchtower saw them and called out that they were coming.

As soon as Samuel saw the tall pointed posts of the palisade he wanted to run, to shout, to cry. He was coming home again! Home with Captain Smith! His master had not forgotten him. He had sent for him, and now he, Samuel Collier, was almost at the gates of Jamestown. As they came nearer and nearer Samuel could see a large crowd standing at the gate. Then he could see Master Smith standing in front of them all.

Smith walked out to meet them with his hand

outstretched. "Sammy, lad," he said, "I have missed you sorely." He took Samuel's arm and walked with him into the fort.

The colonists gathered around, eager to hear the news from Powhatan. Samuel told them all that had happened and what Powhatan had said.

When he finished, Master Smith said, "You have served your country well, Samuel, all Jamestown is proud of you." His arm rested on Samuel's shoulder as the two of them walked toward the house where they had lived together. Samuel looked at the things he had known so well. He felt as if he were looking at old friends he had not seen for a long time.

There were the little streets and there were the little houses. There was the storehouse. Here good Master Hunt lived, and here was the church with the cross upon it.

When they came to their own house, Master Smith opened the door and they went in. At long last Samuel Collier had come home.

VI. CAPTAIN SMITH'S DEPARTURE

That summer was a busy one at Jamestown. Captain Smith had twenty new houses built. He had a well dug inside the fort so the colonists would not have to drink water from the river.

The corn grew tall and green around the fort and the Indians seemed to be quiet. The men at the Glasshouse were hard at work. Some glass had already been sent back to England.

Samuel was busy from sunrise to sunset. Often he copied the letters Master Smith sent back to England. Often he put notices on the board which Master Smith had had made so that each person could see what his work would be for that day. And many times Samuel was called to the gate of the fort to talk to the Indians who came to trade food and skins for hatchets and knives.

News came from London that summer that a fleet of nine ships was coming to Virginia. They would bring men, women and children. They would bring horses and cows and goats. They would bring tools for building and tools for planting.

One of the ships was named the *Sea Venture*. On board it was Sir Thomas Gates, who was sent to be the first governor of Virginia. Before this the head of the colony had been called a president, but now there was to be a governor.

In June and July the colonists looked for the ships but they did not come.

One day in August someone shouted, "They're coming! They're coming! The ships are coming!"

Everyone rushed to the riverside. The James seemed to be full of sails. The colonists counted the ships. One, two, three, four, five, six, seven. Where were the other two?

As the ships came near, the people on the shore saw that masts were broken and sails were ragged and torn. What had happened?

The ships came slowly to the riverbank, gangplanks were lowered and men, women and children came ashore. Two hundred of them!

As soon as the new colonists were safely landed
they began to tell of a terrible storm. It was like
a hurricane. They had seen one ship sink. The
Sea Venture, with the new governor on it, had
disappeared. They did not know what had happened to it.

John Smith looked at all the new settlers and
then he looked at little Jamestown. Where
would he put all of these people? Where would
they live? The new governor was not there to tell
anyone what to do.

Smith decided they would have to build new
towns. He and some other men sailed down the
James to the Bay looking for a good place to build
a town.

Then they sailed up the James to look for a
place. When they came to the place in the river
where the water ran over many rocks, they
landed. The colonists had always called this
place The Falls. Here Smith bought land from

the Indians, and the colonists named the place Nonesuch.

In a few days Smith left Nonesuch and started back to Jamestown. As he was sleeping in his boat that night his powder bag caught fire and exploded.

Smith was badly burned. Ten inches of flesh were torn from his body and his clothes were on fire.

Half asleep and half awake Smith jumped into the river and was almost drowned. One of the men on the ship jumped into the water and pulled him out.

When the boat reached Jamestown Smith seemed more dead than alive. The sailors brought him ashore. There was no doctor to dress his wound or to give him medicine to ease his pain.

When Samuel Collier heard what had happened he went at once to do all he could for his master. He stayed near him day and night. He gave him cool water to drink and he put clean cloths on his wounds.

Some of Smith's friends thought he should go

back to England. They hoped that doctors there could cure him of his hurt. They put Smith on a ship that was getting ready to sail.

Samuel went on board with his master to stay until the ship should start down the James. Richard Wiffin and other good friends went on board to tell Smith goodbye.

Samuel looked down at his master, lying there so white and still. Of all the sad, sad things that had happened at Jamestown this seemed to Samuel the saddest of all. He thought of all the hard work his master had done to keep for England this little piece of land that was Jamestown. And he thought of the many times his master had risked his life that the Colony might not die. And now the brave Captain must go away and leave it all.

Smith looked at Samuel for a minute and then he said, "News has come from England, Samuel, that everyone who serves the colony seven years shall be rewarded. In five more years you will be given 100 acres of land, a house, a garden and an orchard. For two years you have served the colony well. God willing, I hope you will serve it for many more. Heaven and earth never agreed

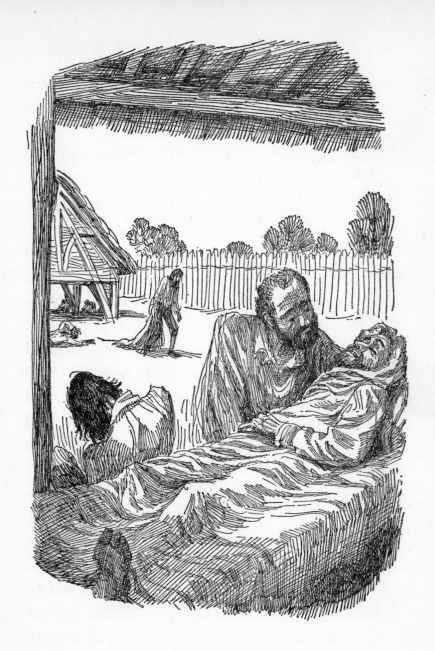

better to frame a place for man's habitation. Virginia is a fruitful and a delightsome land. And who knows, Samuel, but some of us may yet live to see this wilderness an English nation."

For a while Smith stopped speaking, and then he spoke again, "I want you to live with my good and true friend, Richard Wiffin. He will see that you get your just due."

Smith said no more. He had done what he could to make his page's dream of finding his fortune come true.

Samuel's heart was so full that he could not say anything. He held the Captain's hand until he was ordered to go ashore. He stood on the riverbank with his master's friends until the ship's last sail was out of sight.

As they looked out over the water, one of the men said, "We have lost him who ever made justice his first guide. Who hated falsehood and meanness worse than death. Who loved adventure more than words. Who never gave himself more than others. Nor would he send any in danger where he would not go himself."

Samuel turned away from the river and walked

back to the fort with Richard Wiffin. It was hard to believe what he had heard his master say. He, a boy owning nothing in the world, could in five years own a house and 100 acres of land. His master had believed that a boy could do his part to build a colony. Samuel Collier was determined not to disappoint him.

VII. SAMUEL COLLIER: VIRGINIAN

When Captain Smith left for England in October there were over five hundred people at Jamestown. There were horses and pigs and goats and chickens. There were guns and powder, swords and tools.

The Indians always seemed to know what was going on at Jamestown. Powhatan's spies quickly brought him the news that Captain Smith had gone back to England and that he was about to die. This pleased the Indian king, for he and all of his Indians were more afraid of the brave Captain than all the other Englishmen in Jamestown.

The spies also told Powhatan that the ships with many sails had brought men, women and children. When Powhatan heard this he knew the Englishmen had come to stay. They would take his land and cut down his trees. They would frighten the deer and the wild turkeys from the woods with their big guns. And they would frighten the ducks and the geese from the rivers.

Powhatan sent a messenger to all his tribes to tell them what to do. No food was to be traded to the English. Not one basket of corn, not even for guns and swords. The Englishmen must die. He would starve them to death.

Winter came early that year. The days grew shorter and the snow covered the ground. Many of the colonists were sick and cold and hungry. They killed and ate the cows, the pigs, and the goats and the chickens. They killed and ate the horses. Then there was nothing else to kill. And not an Indian would trade one basket of corn.

Whenever the men went into the woods to hunt, Indian arrows flew all around them. Many of the hunters never returned.

Samuel Collier was always hungry. Sometimes

he went alone in the woods to hunt with his Indian bow. One day he killed two wild turkeys and one day he killed a deer. He did not see an Indian and no Indian arrows came near him.

Every day someone died, sometimes more than one. Those who were left ate acorns and roots they dug from the ground. Sometimes they found a few nuts and berries.

At last that terrible winter was over—the terrible winter the colonists would always call the Starving Time.

When the warm spring days came again and the new green leaves came on the trees, only sixty people were living in Jamestown. All of the others had died.

The walls of the fort were falling down. Almost all the houses were empty. The church had no roof. Doors were off their hinges and the people were in rags.

Samuel Collier was one of those who lived. He was tall and thin and he was hungry, hungry, hungry.

The poor, weak, starving colonists wondered if everyone in England had forgotten them. They wondered if help would ever come. Day after day they hoped and looked for a ship.

One day in May two little ships sailed up the James and stopped at Jamestown. Most of the colonists were too sick and too weak to go to the river to see who was coming.

Samuel Collier and a few of the men who could walk staggered down to the shore.

The ships had not come from England; they came from Bermuda.

In the terrible storm the year before the *Sea Venture* had been wrecked on the Bermuda Islands, but all the people had been saved. They lived on the Islands until they could build two little ships. Then they set sail for Jamestown. Sir Thomas Gates, the new governor of Virginia, had come at last.

The passengers came off the ships. They looked at the sick, starving colonists, and they looked at the ruins of Jamestown. They did not want to stay.

The hungry Jamestown colonists begged Sir Thomas Gates to take all of them back to England.

The new Governor looked at the fort and the houses that were falling down. He looked at the tall weeds that grew in the cornfields. He looked at the poor, sick colonists and he decided to take them back to England.

Jamestown was to be abandoned. This little piece of ground where so many had worked and starved and died would become a wilderness again. The cannon were buried at the big gate of the fort. The drums beat a sad roll and all the people went aboard the ships.

Samuel Collier was one of the last to go. He did not want to go. He wanted to stay and work and build. He wanted to claim his house and his land. He wanted to find his fortune in Virginia. Now he would go back and walk the streets of London again with not a penny in his pockets.

The little ships sailed down the James. They left behind them the ruins of Jamestown. They left behind them Samuel Collier's dearest dream. And they left behind them England's only hope for a colony in the New World.

The next day the ships reached the Bay, and in a few hours they would be on the open sea. Suddenly there was a loud cry, "A sail! A sail!"

The passengers rushed on deck. Was it a Spanish ship?

No! No! It was an English ship! It was flying an English flag! Help had come from England at last.

The ship was big. It had many sails. It was loaded with new colonists. It had plenty of food and plenty of supplies. On board was Lord Delaware, come to rule over all Virginia and to make it a strong colony, one that would not fail. Sir Thomas Gates was to be called Lieutenant General. He was to stay and help Lord Delaware rebuild the colony.

The little ships turned around and started back to Jamestown. Samuel Collier was glad, glad. Not only was he going back to Jamestown but the ship had brought the news that Captain John Smith was alive! He was well again and was writing a history of Virginia.

On June 10, 1610, Lord Delaware, the new governor of Virginia, stepped ashore at Jamestown. The drums beat again, a glad rat-a-tat-tat. The color-bearer walked in front of the Lord

Governor, bowing as he went. The flag of England fluttered in the breeze.

The Lord Governor started toward the church. All the colonists followed.

Samuel Collier looked about him as he walked. He had not found gold or pearls. He had been hungry and cold, and sad and afraid. But he loved every stick and every stone of this ground he walked on.

He loved the tall trees and the river flowing by. He loved the green fields of waving corn. He loved the cry of the wild geese in the autumn and the fields of yellow buttercups in the spring. To Samuel and to Captain John Smith, Virginia was a fruitful and a delightsome land. And Samuel still believed that here, some day, he would find his fortune.

They went into the church. The minister raised his hand. Samuel Collier seemed to hear again the same words he had heard three years ago—the words he heard when he first set foot on the land of Virginia.

O Lord we beseech thee mercifully to hear us;

and grant that we, by thy mighty aid, be defended and comforted in all dangers and adversities.

Samuel felt strong and brave. He felt happy and glad. He wanted to work, and struggle, and build. He wanted to see this wilderness become an English nation.

Samuel Collier did work and struggle and build. And he lived to claim his land, his house, his garden and his orchard. He lived to become the "governor of a towne." He knew that the colony he helped to build was growing stronger and stronger. But he never knew that Jamestown in Virginia was the beginning of the United States of America.